How to use this book

Follow the advice, in italics, given for you on each page.
Support the children as they read the text that is shaded in cream.
Praise *the children at every step!*

Detailed guidance is provided in the Read Write Inc. *Handbook*

7 reading activities

Children:

- *practise reading the speed sounds*
- *read the green and red words for the story*
- *listen as you read the introduction*
- *discuss the vocabulary check with you*
- *read the story*
- *re-read the story and discuss the 'questions to talk about'*
- *practise reading the speed words*

LEICESTER
UPLANDS
JUNIOR SCHOOL
EDUCATION AUTHORITY

Read
Write Inc.

An inclusive literacy programme by Ruth Miskin

Speed sounds

Consonants *Say the pure sounds (do not add 'uh')*

f	l	m	n	r	s	v	z	sh	th	ng
ff	ll	mm	nn	rr	ss	ve	zz			nk
			kn		(ce)		s			

b	c	d	g	h	j	p	(qu)	t	w	x	y	ch
bb	k	dd	gg			pp		tt	wh			tch
	(ck)											

Vowels *Say the sounds in and out of order*

at	hen	in	on	up	day	see	high	blow
	head					happy		

zoo	look	car	for	fair	whirl	shout	boy

*Each box contains one sound but sometimes more than one grapheme. Focus graphemes are **circled**.*

Green words

Read in syllables

foll`ow → follow   snow`man → snowman   well`ing`tons → wellingtons

Read the root word first and then with the ending

snow → snowed

Red words

my   you   to

Vocabulary check

Discuss the meaning (as used in the story) after the children have read each word.

definition:

wellingtons   *waterproof boots*

fleece   *extra warm jumper*

glow   *shine warmly (my pink cheeks glow)*

Punctuation to note in this story:

Throw Follow It The   *Capital letters that start sentences*
    Full stop at the end of each sentence

6

Snow

Introduction

Do you love snow? It's so lovely when you wake up in the morning and everything is white. It makes you want to run outside and have a snowball fight or build a snowman.

Story written by Gill Munton
Illustrated by Tim Archbold

Follow me, follow me, into the street.

It snowed last night – see a soft, bright sheet.

Play in the snow with stamping feet.

The snow, the snow, the snow.

Throw a snowball, quick as a jet

Throw it at a snowman – did you hit him yet?

Snow sticks to my wellingtons, soft and wet.

The snow, the snow, the snow.

Three sleepy children, sitting in a row

I'm hot in my fleece and my pink cheeks glow

I throw my hat off, into the snow.

The snow, the snow, the snow.

Questions to talk about

*Re-read the page. Read the question to the children. Tell them whether it is a **FIND IT** question or **PROVE IT** question.*

FIND IT

✓ *Turn to the page*

✓ *Read the question*

✓ *Find the answer*

PROVE IT

✓ *Turn to the page*

✓ *Read the question*

✓ *Find your evidence*

✓ *Explain why*

Page 8:	PROVE IT	*What does the snow look like?*
Page 8:	FIND IT	*What do the children do in the snow?*
Page 10:	PROVE IT	*How fast does the snowball travel?*
Page 12:	FIND IT	*What happens when you get hot playing in the snow?*